Peng

THE PHANTOM OF THE OPERA

GASTON LEROUX

LEVEL

RETOLD FOR THE PENGUIN READERS SERIES
ILLUSTRATED BY DYNAMO LTD
SERIES EDITOR: SORREL PITTS

PENGUIN BOOKS

UK | USA | Canada | Ireland | Australia
India | New Zealand | South Africa

Penguin Books is part of the Penguin Random House group of companies
whose addresses can be found at global.penguinrandomhouse.com.
www.penguin.co.uk www.puffin.co.uk www.ladybird.co.uk

Penguin Readers edition of *The Phantom of the Opera* published by Penguin Books Ltd, 2021
001

Original text written by Gaston Leroux
Text for Penguin Readers edition copyright © Penguin Books Ltd, 2021
Illustrated by Dynamo Ltd
Cover design by La Boco
Illustrations copyright © Penguin Books Ltd, 2021

Printed and bound in Great Britain by Clays Ltd, Elcograf S.p.A.

The authorized representative in the EEA is Penguin Random House Ireland,
Morrison Chambers, 32 Nassau Street, Dublin D02 YH68

A CIP catalogue record for this book is available from the British Library

ISBN: 978−0−241−52064−2

All correspondence to:
Penguin Books
Penguin Random House Children's
One Embassy Gardens, 8 Viaduct Gardens,
London SW11 7BW

Contents

People in the story

Gaston Leroux

The Phantom

Raoul

Christine

The Persian

New words

ball

cables

grave

gunpowder

mask

trapdoor

Note about the story

The **Phantom*** *of the* **Opera** *is* a famous book by the
French writer, Gaston Leroux. He wrote it in 1910. In
Leroux's story, people in Paris, France, are **frightened**
of a phantom. He lives under the Opera House, and
he does bad things. There is a beautiful Opera House
in Paris called the Palais Garnier. But the story of the
phantom is only a story.

Before-reading questions

1 Look for photos of the Opera House in Paris on the
   internet. Answer these questions:
   • Is it old or new?
   • What colours can you see?
   • Is it beautiful?

2 Do you know the names of any opera singers? Listen to
   some European opera music on the internet, for example
   Faust by Charles Gounod. Do you like it?

3 Look at the "People in the story" on page 4.
   a Who is Gaston Leroux?
   b Is the Phantom of the Opera a man or a phantom, do
   you think?
   c Christine is an opera singer at the Opera House in Paris.
   Write about her. Here are some ideas:
      • She is wearing ....
      • She looks about .... years old.
      • She looks happy/sad.

*Definitions of words in **bold** can be found in the glossary on pages 63–64.

CHAPTER ONE
The Opera House

The same evening, there was a new, young singer in an opera.

She's a great singer!

What's her name?

A young man watched the opera.

That's Christine! I knew her in Perros.

CHAPTER TWO
The Phantom

Raoul went to the Opera House every night, but Christine did not sing again.

One day

To Raoul,

I'm sorry. I remember you. I lived in Perros, and I met you.

My father told us stories about the **Angel** of Music. My father is dead now, and I must go to his grave in Perros tomorrow.

Christine

I must go there, too. I love Christine, and I must tell her.

That night Christine went to her father's grave and Raoul went, too.

That music isn't from an angel. It's from a man in a black cloak.

Aargh! His face is a skull …

CHAPTER THREE
The Angel of Music

For two weeks, Raoul didn't see Christine. Then, he went to her home.

Where's Christine?

She's with the Angel of Music.

Christine!

Who is she with?

The next day at Raoul's house

OPERA HOUSE BALL

To Raoul,
Meet me tonight.
Wear a mask.
Christine

Raoul

The next day at Christine's home

Here's Christine. The Angel sent her back to us.

Are you **frightened**, Christine?

Yes, Raoul.

I can help you.

You can't!

Tell me about Erik.

Yes, I heard you. You spoke his name.

Erik?

Christine's story

After a month

Raoul, I'm frightened of Erik!

You must **save** me from him. He's mad.

Let's leave now.

I can't.

Why?

Because I must sing for Erik again tomorrow night. Please listen to my story.

31

The Persian

The next night, Christine was Marguerite and the opera went well.

Ah, my angel, I am coming to you!

Then

The basement

We came to Paris. Erik built the new Opera House.

He lived under it and made secret rooms, trapdoors and a lake.

The torture chamber

43

44

The death of the Phantom

The next day, the Persian was at home.

I found you in the street.

I don't remember.

After four weeks

I had to come.

Erik!

The Opera House, 1910

Workers found a coffin in a basement with a skeleton in it.

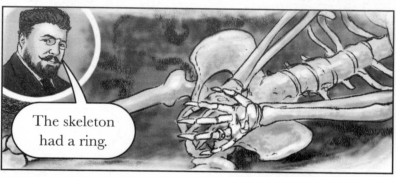

The skeleton had a ring.

Christine was good to Erik. She put the ring on his finger after his death. She put his coffin in the Opera House.

During-reading questions

1 Who killed Joseph?
2 Who is the new opera singer?
3 Does Christine remember Raoul?
4 Who sits in Box Five?

CHAPTER TWO

1 Where does Christine go? Why does she go there?
2 Why does Raoul go there, too?
3 The Angel of Music helps Christine. How does he help her?

CHAPTER THREE

1 Two people love Christine. Who are they?
2 Who must Christine marry?
3 Who is watching Christine and Raoul?

CHAPTER FOUR

1 Why is Christine frightened of Erik?
2 Who is Erik?
3 Where does he live?
4 Erik says to Christine, "Now, you can never leave!"
  Why does he say that?

CHAPTER FIVE

1 Christine cannot leave Paris now. Why not?
2 Christine is singing but then, the next minute, she is not
  there. Where is she?
3 The Persian helps Raoul. How does he help him?
4 Does the Persian hate Erik?

CHAPTER SIX

1 The Persian knows Erik well. How did they meet?
2 What did Erik build for rich and important people?
3 What did Erik build under the Opera House in Paris?

CHAPTER SEVEN

1 Christine can choose the scorpion. What does the scorpion do?
2 Or she can choose the grasshopper. What does the grasshopper do?
3 What must Christine do after Erik's death? (Three things)

CHAPTER EIGHT

1 Why is Erik dying?
2 Did he marry Christine? Why/Why not?
3 What do workers find in the Opera House basement in 1910?

After-reading questions

1 Look at your answer to "Before-reading question 3b". Were you right?
2 What is your favourite part of the story?
3 Who is your favourite person in the story?
4 Why does the phantom wear a mask?
5 Does Christine love the phantom?
6 Is the phantom a nice person?
7 Why does the phantom live in the basement of the Opera House?
8 Are Christine and Raoul happy together after Erik's death, do you think?

Exercises

1 Complete these sentences in your notebook, using the words from the box.

skull	hear	cloak	bad	Box	dark	see

1 He does ....*bad*............ things.
2 His head is a ....
3 He has .... eyes.
4 He wears a long black ....
5 He sits in .... Five.
6 You can .... him but you can't .... him.

CHAPTERS ONE AND TWO

2 Complete these sentences in your notebook, using nouns made from the verbs in the box.

work	sing	teach	direct	write

1 Gaston Leroux is the ....*writer*............ of *The Phantom of the Opera.*
2 Joseph was a .... at the Opera House.
3 Christine is a great opera ....
4 The Opera House has a new ....
5 Christine's singing .... talks to her through a wall.

3 Put these sentences in the correct order in your notebook.

a .... She goes to Perros.
b .... They go to her father's grave.
c .... The Angel of Music plays music.
d ...*1*.... Christine writes to Raoul.
e .... Christine writes to Raoul again.
f .... Raoul goes to Perros.
g .... Christine sings badly.

CHAPTER THREE

4 Are these sentences *true* or *false*? Write the correct
answers in your notebook.

1 Raoul does not see Christine for three weeks. ....*false*..........
2 There is a ball at the Opera House. Lots of people
wear masks.
3 Christine is now wearing a ring.
4 Erik is frightened.
5 Raoul does not love Christine.
6 Christine and Raoul meet every day for one month.

CHAPTER FOUR

5 Match the two parts of these sentences in your
notebook.
Example: 1 – b

1 Christine: I'm frightened of   **a** my face is ugly.
Erik because

2 Christine: I can't leave   **b** he does bad things in the
now because   Opera House.

3 Erik: You must love   **c** you saw my face.
me because

4 Erik: People hate me   **d** I must sing for Erik again
because   tomorrow night.

5 Erik: You can never   **e** then I can finish my music.
leave because

6 **Write the opposites of the bold words in your notebook.**

1 Go **up** those stairs. ....*down*............

2 The Persian is **never** in the Opera House.

3 The next **morning**, Christine is Marguerite in the opera *Faust*.

4 The opera goes **badly**.

5 Do you **love** Erik, too?

7 **Match the words to the pictures in your notebook.**

Example: 1 – c

1   **a** gun

2   **b** trapdoor

3   **c** opera house

4   **d** dressing room

5   **e** torture chamber

6   **f** lake

8 **Choose the correct words to complete the sentences in your notebook.**

1 I don't want *to live* / live / living in the basement now.

2 I can **to hear** / **hear** / **hearing** Christine!

3 I **want** / **wants** / **am wanting** a wife and a nice house.

4 Shh! He **come** / **comes** / **is coming**!

5 She must **choose** / **chose** / **chosen** the scorpion or the grasshopper.

6 Raoul **need** / **needs** / **is needing** water.

CHAPTER EIGHT

9 **Are these sentences *true* or *false*? Write the correct answers in your notebook.**

1 Erik is the Phantom of the Opera. ....*true*...........

2 Erik is the Persian.

3 Erik is the Angel of Music.

4 Erik is a writer of music.

5 Erik is a killer.

6 Erik is a phantom.

7 Erik is a man.

10 **Read the answers, and write the correct question word in your notebook.**

1 ....*Who*........... comes to see the Persian?

Erik comes to see him.

2 Erik does not marry Christine. .... not?

He does not marry her because she does not love him.

3 .... must the Persian do after Erik's death?

He must put "Erik is dead" in the newspaper.

Project work

1 You are Christine or Raoul. Write a letter to a friend, brother, sister or parent. Talk about your life after Erik's death. Where do you live? Do you have any children? What jobs do you do? Are you happy?

2 Choose an opera singer and make a poster about them. Write interesting things about the singer on the poster and put some photos on the poster.

3 Your friend is going to Paris for three days. Look on the internet. What must he or she see in Paris, do you think?

The beautiful city of Paris

Day 1
In the morning, you should go to the Opera House. It is very beautiful. For €14, you can go into the Opera House.
In the afternoon, . . .

Day 2
. . .

Day 3
. . .

An answer key for all questions and exercises can be found at
www.penguinreaders.co.uk

Glossary

ago (adv.)
Yesterday was one day *ago*.

angel (n.)
In stories, *angels* live in the sky.
They are good. They help
people.

build (v.)
to make a house, for example

choose (v.)
You can have this thing or this
thing. You must *choose*.

dead (adj.); **death** (n.)
A person dies. It is their *death*.
Then that person is not living.
The person is *dead*.

director (n.)
The *director* is an important
person in a place.

escape (v.)
to run from a person or place

frightened (adj.)
People are *frightened* of dark
places, bad people and *phantoms*.

hate (v.)
You *hate* a person or thing
because you do not like it.

jump (v.)
to push your body above the
ground with your legs and feet

leaving (v.)
to go from a place

mad (adj.)
not well in the head

marry (v.)
to start to be husband and wife

opera (n.)
In an *opera*, people tell a story
in songs. They sing very well.
Many people watch and listen.

palace (n.)
A *palace* is a big, beautiful
house.

phantom (n.)
In stories, people die and come
back as *phantoms*.

poor (adj.)
You say '*poor*' before a person's
name. You feel sad for them.

save (v.)
A person *escapes* from a bad
person or thing because you
help them.

secret (adj.)
Only some people know about
a *secret* thing. Other people do
not know about it. You must not
talk about *secret* things.

torture chamber (n.)
a very bad place. You can go
mad in a *torture chamber*.

trust (v.)
You *trust* a person. You know
them well. They are always
good.